Once a Week
Comprehension

Haydn Perry

GW00567945

Book 1

Ginn is an imprint of Pearson Education Limited, a company incorporated in England and Wales, having its registered office at Edinburgh Gate, Harlow, Essex, CM20 2JE. Registered company number: 872828

www.ginn.co.uk

Text © Haydn Perry, 1960

This revised edition 2008

12 11
10 9 8 7 6

British Library Cataloguing in Publication Data is available from the British Library on request.

ISBN 978 0 435996 72 7

Copyright notice
All rights reserved. No part of this publication may be reproduced in any form or by any means (including photocopying or storing it in any medium by electronic means and whether or not transiently or incidentally to some other use of this publication) without the written permission of the copyright owner, except in accordance with the provisions of the Copyright, Designs and Patents Act 1988 or under the terms of a licence issued by the Copyright Licensing Agency, Saffron House, 6–10 Kirby Street, London EC1N 8TS (www.cla.co.uk). Applications for the copyright owner's written permission should be addressed to the publisher.

Typeset by Planman Technologies India Pvt. Ltd
Cover design by Tony Richardson
Cover photo © iStockphoto.com
Printed by Multivista Global Ltd

Every effort has been made to contact copyright holders of material reproduced in this book. Any omissions will be rectified in subsequent printings if notice is given to the publishers.

PREFACE

This book of thirty comprehension pieces is intended to develop the intensive reading ability of children of the middle primary school years. The passages are graded in difficulty. They are followed by questions that test the student's understanding of the text, and by a wide range of language exercises aimed at improving grammar and composition skills, and increasing the student's vocabulary.

TO THE PUPIL

In each of the thirty tests there are five questions.

Read each question carefully, so that you understand exactly what you are asked to do before you begin.

Do not spend too long on any one question. You should answer all five questions in 45 minutes.

Make sure that you have not missed a question, or part of one.

If you find that you have made a mistake, alter your work clearly and neatly so that your teacher will know what it is you mean him or her to read and mark.

HAYDN PERRY

A NOTE FROM THE PUBLISHERS

In this new edition, each of the exercises has been given a heading to help students identify the topics they are working on. Some of the passages and exercises have also been edited to ensure that the content and usage of language are up to date.

TEST 1

(A) Read through the following passage very carefully, and then answer the questions.

The Tin Soldier

There were four-and-twenty tin soldiers, all brothers, for they had all been made from one old, tin spoon. They wore red and blue uniforms, carried muskets in their arms, and held themselves very upright.

The first words they heard in the world, when the lid was taken off the box in which they lay, were 'Tin soldiers!' It was a little boy who said this, clapping his hands at the same time. The soldiers had been given to him because it was his birthday. He now set them out on the table. The soldiers resembled each other to a hair, all except one who was rather different from the rest, for he had been made last, when there was not quite enough tin left. He stood as firmly upon one tin leg as the others did upon two.

1   Were the soldiers made from: (*a*) a silver spoon; (*b*) a wooden spoon; (*c*) a tin spoon?
2   How do we know that they were all of one family?
3   What did the soldiers wear?
4   What did the little boy say?
5   Was he (*a*) unhappy; (*b*) not very interested; (*c*) very happy indeed?
6   Why was he given the soldiers?
7   Which part of one soldier was missing?
8   Why was this?
9   Which words tell us that the soldiers were exactly alike?
10   The one-legged soldier always: (*a*) stood upright; (*b*) lay down on his back; (*c*) knelt beside the cannon.
11   Were the soldiers, when given to the little boy, (*a*) in a brown paper parcel; (*b*) in a plastic bag; (*c*) in a box?

(B) Opposites

The word **young** is the opposite of the word **old**.

Example: *The puppy was **young** but the dog was **old**.*

Write out the sentences below using the opposite of the word in heavy type each time to fill the space.

1 Tom was **slow** at his work, but Jim was _____.
2 This book is **cheap**, but that one is _____.
3 Ann is **tall**, and Jane is _____.
4 Is your answer **right** or _____?

(C) Punctuation

Punctuation marks (, . ?) are missing from the following sentences. Write the sentences with the correct marks in them.

1 Where do you live
2 Dad needs an axe a saw and a hammer
3 Do peas beans and carrots make a tasty meal
4 Can we buy ice lollies and lemonade at the fair

(D) Gender

Change the following sentences, which are about men, making them about women.

1 The **man** is in the park.
2 The **boy** rode the horse.
3 **He** bought a book.
4 The **widower** lived alone.

(E) Making new words

If we chop the first letter off the name of a fruit – PEAR – we get that with which we hear – EAR. (PEAR becomes EAR.)

Do the same with these:

1 'A horse's home' becomes 'that at which we eat our meals'.
2 'That with which we sweep' becomes 'part of any house'.
3 'That which grows on our head and skin' becomes 'something that we breathe'.

TEST 2

(A) Read through the following passage very carefully, and then answer the questions.

The Lion and the Mouse

A lion was sleeping outside his den when a mouse, not knowing where he was going, ran over the mighty beast's nose and woke him. The lion clapped his paw upon the mouse and was about to make an end of him; but the mouse begged the lion to spare his life, and promised one day to pay him back for his kindness. So the lion let the mouse go.

Some time later, the lion found himself caught in a hunter's trap. He tried to free himself but could not do so. His roars echoed through the forest, and the mouse came running to see what was happening. He set to work to nibble through the net that held the lion prisoner, and in a short time he was able to set him free. In this way he repaid the great beast's kindness.

1 The mouse ran over the lion's nose: (*a*) to show how brave he was; (*b*) to make the lion angry; (*c*) quite by accident.

2 The lion was: (*a*) prowling in the forest; (*b*) eating his prey; (*c*) sleeping peacefully.

3 What did the lion mean to do with the mouse?

4 How did the mouse manage to make the lion set him free?

5 In which was the lion caught: (*a*) an iron cage; (*b*) a pit in the ground; (*c*) a net?

6 How did the mouse know that the lion was caught?

7 How did he set the lion free?

8 Which of these makes the best title for the story? (*a*) An Apple a Day Keeps the Doctor Away (*b*) One Good Turn Deserves Another (*c*) Empty Vessels Make the Most Sound

(B) Odd one out

In each of the following groups of the following, one word is out of place because it has nothing to do with the others.

Example: *pen, pencil, ruler, dog.*

Dog is the odd one out, for the others all have to do with writing.

Find the odd one out in these:

1   leg, arm, foot, paw
2   terrier, corgi, kitten, spaniel
3   cocoa, water, coffee, tea
4   rough, clean, neat, tidy

(C) This is to that

Example: **Finger** *is to* **hand** *as* **toe** *is to* **foot**.

Now do these:

1   **Little** is to **big**, as **short** is to _____.
2   **Dog** is to **puppy**, as **fox** is to _____.
3   **Cry** is to **sad**, as **laugh** is to _____.
4   **Oar** is to **boat**, as **pedal** is to _____.

(D) Alphabetical order

Here are the names of eight fruits. Write them down in alphabetical order.

date, fig, apple, pear, raspberry, strawberry, banana, pineapple.

(E) Anagrams

Look at the four letters E D A L. With these four letters we can make several words. Here are some clues:

1   This is another name for a valley.
2   We do this when playing cards.
3   We find this inside pencils.

Now look at the four letters E M N A. With these four letters we can make the following words:

4   Christians say this at the end of a prayer.
5   A horse has one.
6   Everyone in the world has one.

TEST 3

(A) Read through the following passage very carefully, and then answer the questions.

The Wolf and the Lamb

A wolf one day was drinking at a stream when he spied a lamb who was also refreshing herself farther down. The wolf made up his mind to eat the lamb, but he thought that he would find some excuse before doing so. He ran up to the lamb, and said, 'How dare you muddy the water that I am drinking!' The lamb replied, 'I do not see how that can be, since the water of the stream is running from you to me, and not from me to you.'

The wolf then said, 'Last year you called me many nasty names.' 'But that cannot be,' replied the lamb, 'for I was not born last year.' 'Then if it was not you, it was your father. It is no use making excuses,' cried the wolf. With that he sprang upon the helpless lamb and devoured her.

1 How do we know that the wolf and the lamb were not standing in the stream side by side?
2 When the wolf saw the lamb, what did he make up his mind to do?
3 But what did he think he would do first?
4 The wolf said to the lamb: (*a*) 'You are drinking all the water.' (*b*) 'I am afraid to come near the stream.' (*c*) 'You are making the water muddy for me.'
5 How did the lamb prove that the wolf was wrong?
6 The wolf then said: (*a*) 'You broke into my den.' (*b*) 'You said unkind things about me.' (*c*) 'You stole some meat from me.'
7 How did the lamb show that this was untrue?
8 What happened to the lamb in the end?

B **Put in order**

The words in each of the following are in the wrong order. Rearrange them to make sentences. Remember to capitalise the correct word.

1 barks dog the loudly.
2 coat hangs the peg the on.
3 boots school wore he to his.
4 currant there's cake tea for.

C **Crossword puzzles**

Use the clues to find the words. They each begin with WAR.

1 To sing like a bird.   WAR _ _ _
2 A soldier or fighter.   WAR _ _ _ _
3 Where many rabbits live.   WAR _ _ _
4 A person who works in a prison. WAR _ _ _
5 Part of any hospital.   WAR _

D **Synonyms**

The three words in the first brackets all have similar meanings. Choose one word from those in the second brackets that is also similar in meaning to those in the first brackets.

Example: (*flock, herd, swarm*) – (*thunder, troop, summer*)

1 (sleek, velvety, smooth) – (glossy, ugly, rough)
2 (fog, mist, vapour) – (people, animals, cloud)
3 (jam, syrup, honey) – (timber, treacle, grass)
4 (mutter, mumble, murmur) – (whisper, cry, shout)

E **Animal movements**

One of the words in this list fits into each of the following sentences.

    hops   trots   prowls   soars   bounds

1 The deer _____ over the heather.
2 The donkey _____ on the sands.
3 The wren _____ on the lawn.
4 The lion _____ in the forest.
5 The lark _____ in the sky.

TEST 4

(A) Read through the following passage very carefully, and then answer the questions.

The Three Brothers

The whole of a certain little valley belonged to three brothers called Schwartz, Hans and Gluck. The two elder brothers were very ugly men. They lived by farming the Treasure Valley. They killed everything that did not pay for what it ate. They shot the blackbirds because they pecked the fruit. They killed the hedgehogs in case they worried the cows in the fields. They poisoned the crickets for eating the crumbs in the kitchen. They made the servants work for no wages until they would not work any more, and then they turned them out of doors without paying them.

The youngest brother, Gluck, was very different from the others. He was twelve years old, fair, blue-eyed, and kind to everything that was living.

1   What were the names of the three brothers?
2   What did they own?
3   Were the brothers (*a*) farmers; (*b*) workers in a factory; (*c*) cobblers?
4   Which of the brothers were ugly and cruel?
5   Why did they kill the birds and animals around them?
6   They killed the blackbirds by _____ them.
7   They killed the crickets by _____ them.
8   They paid their servants: (*a*) high wages; (*b*) nothing at all; (*c*) very little.
9   How was Gluck different from his brothers?

B Complete the story

These words are missing from the story below:

sparkled	beautiful	prince	thorny
fountain	garden	beds	lawns

Write out the story, putting the words in the correct places.

At last the _____ cut his way through the _____ hedge and entered the _____. There were trim green _____, and _____ flowers were growing in the _____. A _____ was playing and its waters _____ in the sunlight.

C Making new words

Each of the unfinished words in the sentences below ends in **age**. What are these words?

1 The budgerigar had beautiful _ _ _ _ **age**.
2 The _ _ _ _ **age** on this parcel will not be much.
3 They had a fine meal of bacon and _ _ _ _ **age**.
4 The _ _ _ _ **age** was loaded into the car.

D Choose the correct word

Rewrite the following sentences, choosing the correct word from those given.

1 How did you know it **was/were** me?
2 All of you **is/are** at fault.
3 The girls **is/are** certain to be chosen.
4 None of you **are/is** to come.

E Homophones

Some words sound the same, but are spelt differently.
Example: *The plane/plain flew over the house.*
The correct word is **plane**. The other word **plain** means 'flat ground'.
Choose the correct word each time.

1 The miners found iron **oar/ore** in the mountains.
2 Things are not what they **seem/seam**.
3 I'll tell you a **tail/tale** of the sea.
4 Sage and **time/thyme** grew in the garden.
5 The **sent/scent** of roses filled the air.

TEST 5

(A) Read through the following verses very carefully, and then answer the questions.

The Pedlar's Caravan

I wish I lived in a caravan
With a horse to drive, like a pedlar-man!
Where he comes from nobody knows,
Or where he goes to, but on he goes.

His caravan has windows two,
And a chimney of tin that the smoke comes through;
He has a wife, and a baby brown,
And they go riding from town to town.

Chairs to mend, and delft to sell!
He clashes the basins like a bell;
Tea-trays, baskets ranged in order,
Plates, with the alphabet round the border.

W. B. Rands

1 Where had the caravan come from? (*a*) no one can tell; (*b*) from the Land of Nod; (*c*) from over the sea from Skye.
2 How did it move from place to place? (*a*) It was a motor caravan. (*b*) It was drawn by a horse. (*c*) It was a trailer behind a car.
3 What kind of person lived in the caravan: (*a*) a rich merchant; (*b*) a man on holiday; (*c*) a man selling things?
4 How can we tell that he was able to mend broken things?
5 What were the plates like: (*a*) plain white; (*b*) blue all over; (*c*) decorated with letters?
6 Write down the sentences that are true: (*a*) The pedlar was married. (*b*) He had to cook outside. (*c*) He had no children. (*d*) He was a bachelor. (*e*) He could make a fire inside the caravan. (*f*) He could see out of the caravan.

(B) Similes

Look at this: *David's tea was **as sweet as** _____*. The missing word is **honey**, because the saying is that sweet things are 'as sweet as honey'.

Finish these sentences, using the correct words:

1 The water was **as cold as** _____.
2 Linda was **as quiet as a** _____.
3 Mary's first cake was **as heavy as** _____.
4 After the race, Paul was **as fresh as a** _____.

(C) Compound words

Here are two words: **gold** and **fish**. If we put them together we can make a new word **goldfish**.

From these eight words make four new words, using each once only:

night	mine	house	field
back	work	time	pack

(D) Collective nouns

We speak of a **string** of **beads**. What words might we use to fill these spaces?

1 A _____ of grapes.
2 A _____ of clothes.
3 A _____ of cards.
4 A _____ of furniture.
5 A _____ of footballers.

(E) Crossword puzzles

Here are some crossword-puzzle clues. The answer to each clue begins with QU.

1 Where ships sometimes tie up.   QU _ _
2 Arrows are carried in this.   QU _ _ _ _
3 When people do not agree.   QU _ _ _ _ _
4 Half of a half.   QU _ _ _ _ _
5 The wife of a king.   QU _ _ _

TEST 6

(A) Read through the following passage very carefully, and then answer the questions.

The Dog and the Bone

A dog who had stolen a juicy bone from a butcher's shop was hurrying into the country where he hoped to enjoy his meal. He came to a bridge that crossed a stream. As he was passing over, he looked down into the water where he saw what he thought was a second dog also carrying a bone. He made up his mind to have that bone as well.

When he stopped, the other dog stopped. When he moved, so did the other. This went on for some time, until the dog on the bridge could stand it no longer. He gave a fierce bark, hoping to scare his enemy. To his dismay, the bone dropped from his own jaws and disappeared below the surface of the stream. When the water cleared, and he looked down, there was the other dog looking up at him. Strangely enough, he had no bone in his jaws.

1   How do we know that the dog had not been given the bone as a present?
2   How do we know that the bone was a very fine one?
3   Where was the dog taking the bone?
4   The dog: (*a*) had to swim across the stream; (*b*) crossed it with a flying leap; (*c*) passed over it on a bridge.
5   Why did he give a fierce bark?
6   What happened when he did this?
7   'To his dismay': Does this mean: (*a*) he was happy; (*b*) he was very unhappy; (*c*) he didn't care very much?
8   Why did the other dog do exactly the same?

(B) More than one

The sentence 'The key will not fit the lock' means **one** key and **one** lock. But the sentence 'The **keys** will not fit the **locks**' means **more than one** key and **more than one** lock.

Change the sentences below so that they mean more than one.

1 The daisy grew in the hedge.
2 The mouse hid in the wall.
3 The tooth of the tiger shone white.
4 The woman went shopping.
5 He cut his foot on the stone.

(C) Spot the mistakes

There are mistakes in each of these sentences. Write the sentences correctly by changing the wrong word.

1 Mother has gone to lay down.
2 The player done his best.
3 Teasing a cat makes them angry.
4 I cannot find it nowhere.
5 I seen him at the football match.

(D) Using one word

Write the following sentences, but use one word instead of the words in heavy type.

1 This is the **way in**.
2 The coat is **one that keeps out the rain**.
3 The witch was **not able to be seen**.
4 The warder came to **set free** the prisoners.

(E) Rhyming words

The words **out** and **shout** have the same sound. We call them rhyming words.

Write these eight words in pairs, so that they rhyme:

| cheap | route | quest | sleep |
| queen | pest | scene | boot |

TEST 7

(A) Read through the following passage very carefully, and then answer the questions.

Great Claus and Little Claus

Once upon a time there lived in a village two men who had the same name, Claus. One of them owned four horses, while the other had only one. So the owner of the four horses was called Great Claus, and the other was known as Little Claus.

All the week Little Claus had to plough for Great Claus, and lend him his one horse. In return, on Sunday, Great Claus would lend Little Claus his four horses. A proud man then was Little Claus. The people looked at him as he brandished his whip over the five horses. He was so pleased that he kept cracking his whip and crying out again and again 'Hip, hip, hurrah! Five fine horses and all of them mine!'

'You must not say that,' said Great Claus. 'Only one of the horses is yours. You know that well enough.'

1 How do we know that the two men lived near each other?
2 Why was one called Great Claus, and the other called Little Claus?
3 What were the horses used for?
4 On which days did Little Claus work for Great Claus?
5 Why was Little Claus so happy on Sunday?
6 What did Little Claus shout out that was not true?
7 Why did this make Great Claus angry?
8 Which words in the story tell us that (*a*) he waved his whip; (*b*) he made a noise with his whip; (*c*) everyone was watching him?
9 Which of these makes the best title for the story? (*a*) The Farmers of England (*b*) Little Claus is Careless with his Words (*c*) The Happy Brothers

(B) **Abbreviations and contractions**

In these sentences you will see some short ways of writing words. They are shown in heavy type. Write out these shortened words in full:

1 At the bottom of the page he saw **PTO**.
2 Run and call **Dr** Smith.
3 **Nov.** 30th is **St** Andrew's Day.
4 Peter lives at 1 Sherwood **Ave**.

(C) **Word-doubles**

We call 'this and that' a word-double.
*They talked about **this and that**.*

Finish the word-doubles in the sentences below.

1 The clock's pendulum swung **to and** _____.
2 The box is full of **odds and** _____.
3 Jim landed **safe and** _____.
4 All creatures **great and** _____ are welcome.

(D) **Put in order**

Here are three sentences from a story, but they are not in the order in which things happened. Write them in the correct order.

1 They were then laid in a row on the table.
2 The dolls were taken from the cupboard.
3 The largest and prettiest was finally chosen.

(E) **Adding a letter**

If we add a letter to PIN, we make the word PINT. In the same way, add a letter to the words below.

The letter may be added anywhere in the word.

1 LAP becomes **a jump**.
2 TROT becomes **a fish**.
3 CAP becomes **a piece of land sticking out into the sea**.
4 LAST becomes **the sound of an explosion**.
5 RAG becomes **anger**.
6 OAT becomes **a vessel**.

TEST 8

(A) Read through the following passage very carefully, and then answer the questions.

The Crow and the Cheese

A crow one day found a large piece of cheese and flew away with it to a tall tree where she meant to make a meal. A hungry fox passing by saw the crow with the cheese in her beak, and made up his mind to have the tasty food for himself.

'O crow,' he said in his gentlest tones, 'all the folk of the forest tell me what a charming voice you have, and how very sweetly you sing. Pray, let me hear you warble one of your delightful tunes.'

The crow felt very flattered at hearing this praise from the fox, so she opened her beak to sing. At once, the cheese fell to the ground, whereupon the cunning fox grabbed the titbit and hurried away to his den to enjoy his meal, leaving the foolish crow in the treetop, sadder and wiser, and of course hungry.

1   How did the crow come to have the cheese?
2   Where did she go to eat it?
3   When the fox saw the cheese, what did he wish to do?
4   What did he ask the crow to do?
5   When did the cheese fall to the ground?
6   Where did the fox go to have his meal?
7   Why was the crow 'sadder and wiser': (*a*) because she had no one to sing to; (*b*) because the tree had fallen; (*c*) because she had lost the cheese?
8   'The crow was flattered' means: (*a*) she was very pleased; (*b*) she was smashed flat by a branch; (*c*) she ate the cheese and grew fat.
9   Write down all the words that are used in the story to describe the cheese.

B Opposites

The word **big** is the opposite of the word **small**.

Example: *Tom was big but Jim was small.*

Write out these sentences using the opposite of the word in heavy type each time to fill the space:

1 The horse was **strong**, but the donkey was _____.
2 The king is **rich**, but the pauper is _____.
3 The troops will **defend** the fort against _____.
4 Why is this painting so **pretty**, but that painting so _____?

C Alphabetical order

Here are the names of eight vegetables. Write them down in alphabetical order.

marrow, carrot, parsnip, turnip, bean, swede, onion, leek.

D Odd one out

In each of the following groups of words, one word is out of place because it has nothing to do with the others.

Example: *girls, ladies, lads, maidens.*

Lads is the odd one out, because all the others are female.

Find the odd one out in these:

1 cup, saucer, saucepan, plate
2 bicycle, sleigh, sledge, toboggan
3 sword, dagger, shield, lance
4 knife, plate, fork, spoon

E This is to that

Example: *Toe is to foot as finger is to hand.*

Now do these:

1 **Stable** is to **horse** as **kennel** is to _____.
2 **Stone** is to **solid** as **water** is to _____.
3 **Tall** is to **short** as **fat** is to _____.
4 **Bark** is to **tree** as **feathers** are to _____.

TEST 9

(A) Read through the following passage very carefully, and then answer the questions.

The Good Fairy Helps Cinderella

As soon as the Good Fairy waved her wand, the pumpkin became a coach, and the six white mice became ponies. It was now time for Cinderella to leave for the Royal Palace where the ball was to be held. The two Ugly Sisters had gone on ahead, not dreaming that Cinderella would follow. They thought that she would be sitting sadly at the hearth, or doing the cleaning.

When Cinderella walked down the marble staircase, the Prince's eyes opened wide in surprise. Never had he seen such a beautiful damsel. He crossed the ballroom and, bowing low before her, he asked her to dance with him. The band struck up a tune. The handsome Prince and the beautiful maiden waltzed happily round the room, while the onlookers gazed in wonder. Whoever could this be who had stolen the heart of their Prince Charming?

1   Where was the ball taking place?
2   When did the pumpkin become a coach?
3   What had the horses once been?
4   'The band struck up a tune.' Did the band (*a*) begin to fight; (*b*) go on strike for more pay; (*c*) begin to play music?
5   Write down the sentences that are true: (*a*) The staircase was made of wood. (*b*) No one knew who Cinderella was. (*c*) The Prince took no notice of her. (*d*) The staircase was a stone one. (*e*) The Prince asked Cinderella to dance with him. (*f*) The people looking on knew who Cinderella was.
6   Find words that mean: (*a*) girl; (*b*) fireside; (*c*) people looking on.

Ⓑ Put in order

The words in each of the following are in the wrong order. Rearrange them to make sentences. Remember to capitalise the correct word.

1 The tree Jack climbed tall.
2 Peter the goal scored only.
3 Let me mother it take.
4 Outer man came from space the.

Ⓒ Complete the story

These words are missing from the story below:

| gazed | wondered | thick | sign |
| happen | moon | rocket | craters |

Write out the story, putting the words in the correct spaces.

The _____ was now near to the _____. Nothing could be seen but _____. There was no _____ of life. The men _____ through the _____ glass and _____ what would _____ next.

Ⓓ Prepositions

Look at these words: **at, in, into, behind, beside**. Write the correct one in the space in each sentence below.

1 The friends sat _____ one another.
2 The coin fell _____ the wishing well.
3 The book was _____ the cupboard.
4 Sally aimed _____ the target.
5 In the race, Roger was just _____ the winner.

Ⓔ Anagrams

Look at the four letters R S A T. With these four letters we can make different words. Here are some clues:

1 It twinkles in the sky.
2 Rodents, often blamed for carrying disease.

Do the same with these four letters: T S O P.

3 We spin these.
4 _____ and pans.
5 This stands in the ground.

TEST 10

(A) Read through the following verses very carefully, and then answer
the questions.

Queen Mab

A little fairy comes at night,
Her eyes are blue, her hair is brown,
With silver spots upon her wings;
And from the moon she flutters down.

She has a little silver wand,
And when a good child goes to bed,
She waves her wand from right to left
And makes a circle round its head.

And then it dreams of pleasant things,
Of fountains filled with fairy fish;
And trees that bear delicious fruit,
And bow their branches at a wish.

Thomas Hood

1 Where does the little fairy come from?
2 Which of these does the poem say? (*a*) She rides on a moth's
back. (*b*) She travels on a broomstick. (*c*) She flies down.
3 Are her wings (*a*) quite plain in colour; (*b*) decorated with
silver spots; (*c*) marked in gold and green stripes?
4 For what purpose does she use the wand: (*a*) to ride upon;
(*b*) to beat time to the music; (*c*) to weave her magic spells?
5 Write down the sentences that are true: (*a*) The child dreams
of lovely things. (*b*) The wand is waved up and down.
(*c*) The fountains are filled with frogs and toads. (*d*) The wand
is waved from right to left. (*e*) The child has horrid dreams.
(*f*) There are pretty fish in the fountains.
6 What do the trees do to make the child happy: (*a*) give it
shade; (*b*) bring their branches low so that it can reach the
fruit; (*c*) give it wood for its bonfire?

B **Using one word**

Write these sentences, but use one word instead of the words in heavy type:

1 He wrote the letter **with great care**.
2 **By good luck** he saw the sign.
3 Come **at once**.
4 He saw the Roman remains in the **building for storing things of the past**.

C **Who does what?**

Write the correct definition for each of the words in heavy type.

1 A **pilot**   (*a*) sells pies; (*b*) flies planes and other aircraft; (*c*) fixes lights.
2 A **stationer**   (*a*) looks after a railway station; (*b*) always stands still; (*c*) sells pens, ink, writing-paper, etc.
3 A **sculptor**   (*a*) carves models from wood or stone; (*b*) grows food for sale; (*c*) collects old books.
4 A **locksmith**   (*a*) looks after a prison; (*b*) locks up a man named Smith; (*c*) makes and repairs locks of doors.

D **Choose the correct word**

Rewrite the following sentences, choosing the correct word from those given.

1 Only one of us **are/is** able to come.
2 Jill and Robin **were/was** older than the twins.
3 All the apples **was/were** green.
4 Pam's doll **were/was** broken the next day.

E **Prefixes**

Look at these two sentences: *Dick was **happy**. Bill was **unhappy**.* By adding **un** to **happy** the word becomes the exact opposite in meaning.

Do the same with these sentences. To make the opposite in each case, choose from these parts of words: **un**, **in**, **dis**, **im**.

1 I **like** carrots but I _____ onions.
2 This chair is **comfortable**; that chair is _____.
3 Her sum is **correct**, but yours is _____.
4 You think it **possible**, but I think it is _____.

TEST 11

(A) Read through the following passage very carefully, and then answer the questions.

The Hare and the Tortoise

Once, a hare and a tortoise began to argue as to which of them was the faster. They decided to run a race over a certain distance. Almost as soon as they started, the hare was far ahead and out of sight, whilst the tortoise had gone only a few yards.

The hare now thought he would take things easy. He lay down to have a nap until the tortoise could catch up with him. But the tortoise plodded on and on. The hare overslept and awoke with a start. In the distance he could see the tortoise, who had passed him while he was asleep, very near to the winning-post. He ran with might and determination in an effort to be first, but the slow-moving tortoise crawled past the finishing line some yards in front of the much speedier hare.

1. What were the hare and the tortoise quarrelling about?
2. How did they decide to settle the quarrel?
3. Why was the hare far ahead whilst the tortoise had gone only a few yards?
4. Explain why the hare lay down to have a nap.
5. What happened while he was asleep?
6. How do we know that the hare did not really mean to sleep so long?
7. By how much did the tortoise beat the hare?
8. Which words or phrases in the story mean: (*a*) as fast as he could; (*b*) went along very slowly; (*c*) far away; (*d*) made up their minds; (*e*) the place where the race ended?
9. Which of these makes the best title for the story? (*a*) Harry Hare Beat Tommy Tortoise (*b*) Runner Beats Crawler (*c*) Slow but Sure is the Winner

(B) Similes

Look at this: *Peter was **as slow as a** _____.* The missing word is
tortoise, because we often say that slow people or things are like
the tortoise.

Finish these sentences, using the correct word:

1   During the games lesson, Susan was **as playful as a** _____.
2   While the teacher was away, the class was **as good as** _____.
3   The footballer marking Bob was **as tall as a** _____.
4   The judge was **as wise as an** _____.

(C) Making new words

If we chop the first letter off the name of an **animal** – FOX – we
get **another animal** – OX. (FOX becomes OX.) Do the same with
these:

1   'To begin' becomes a sort of 'fruit pie'.
2   'Daring, and full of adventure' becomes 'getting on in years'.
3   'A group of sheep' becomes 'that which fastens a door'.
4   'Something we sit on' becomes 'that which grows on our
    heads'.

(D) Adding a letter

If we add a letter to PIN, we make the word SPIN. In the same
way, add a letter to the words below. The letter may be added anywhere in the word.

1   TEAM becomes **what is given off when water boils**.
2   PAWN becomes **a sea creature**.
3   WAIT becomes **part of the body where a belt is worn**.
4   PLAN becomes **a level piece of land**.

(E) Word endings

Write down the complete words in these sentences. Each one ends
in either **tion** or **sion**.

1   The next lesson will be **dicta** _ _ _ _.
2   When you are old you will have a **pen** _ _ _ _.
3   The baron lived in a great **man** _ _ _ _.
4   I want a work of **fic** _ _ _ _ from the library.

TEST 12

(A) Read through the following passage very carefully, and then answer the questions.

Alice and the White Rabbit (*retold*)

Alice was very tired of sitting by her sister on the bank, and having nothing to do. Once or twice she had peeped into the book her sister was reading, but it had no pictures in it, 'and what is the use of a book,' thought Alice, 'without pictures!'

Suddenly a white rabbit with pink eyes ran close by her. There was nothing so very remarkable in that. Nor did Alice think it so very much out of the way to hear the rabbit say to itself 'Oh dear! Oh dear! I shall be too late!' But when the rabbit took a watch out of its waistcoat pocket, and looked at it, and then hurried on, Alice started to her feet. It flashed across her mind that she had never before seen a rabbit with either a waistcoat pocket, or a watch to take out of it.

1 Was Alice: (*a*) tired of reading her book; (*b*) tired of playing with her doll; (*c*) tired of doing nothing?
2 Was Alice sitting: (*a*) in her mother's garden; (*b*) on a bench in the park; (*c*) on a river bank?
3 Why didn't she like the book her sister was reading?
4 Write down the sentences that are true: (*a*) The rabbit was black. (*b*) It wore a dark green overcoat. (*c*) It spoke to itself. (*d*) It scurried along. (*e*) It carried an umbrella. (*f*) It strolled along calmly. (*g*) It wore a waistcoat. (*h*) It was a white rabbit.
5 By what means did the rabbit tell the time?
6 'Alice started to her feet'. Does this mean: (*a*) she was ready to run in a race; (*b*) she stood up quickly; (*c*) she put her shoes and stockings on?

B Crossword puzzles

Here are some crossword-puzzle clues. What are the answers?

1	To fly into the air.	SO _ _
2	Helpless and timid.	WE _ _
3	Where the ship begins its trip.	P _ _ R
4	We travel along this.	RO _ _
5	Grows at the edge of a lake.	RE _ _

C A or An?

Example: *a boy*, *a glass*, **an apple**, **an egg**.

Write **a** or **an** in the spaces in the sentences below.

1 _____ angry sea beat on _____ rocky shore.
2 He saw _____ antelope and _____ zebra.
3 _____ hunter shot _____ elk.
4 _____ accident happened in _____ school.

D Answer the questions

Write down the answers to the following questions.

1 What do we call a place where a car is kept?
2 What is the front part of a ship called?
3 What would I expect a caddie to do for me?
4 Where would two boxers fight?

E Common phrases

1 She said to Richard, 'It's time you turned over a new leaf.' Did she mean: (*a*) start a new page in the exercise book; (*b*) get on with the gardening; (*c*) behave much better than he had done?
2 She said to a footballer, 'Just play the game.' Did she mean: (*a*) play the game fairly and according to the rules; (*b*) free kick to the other team; (*c*) get on with the game?
3 She said to Brian, 'You've put your foot in it.' Did she mean: (*a*) tried the water in the swimming-pool; (*b*) stepped into a cage; (*c*) given himself away, or done something foolish?

TEST 13

(A) Read through the following passage very carefully, and then answer the questions.

The Woodman's Axe

One day a poor woodman was cutting a tree on the bank of a river. By chance his iron axe slipped from his hand, fell into the water and sank immediately. The woodman sat down and began to cry about his loss. The fairy who lived in the river, feeling sorry for him, dived to the bottom and brought up a golden axe. But the honest woodman said that it was not his. The river-fairy dived again and this time brought up a silver axe; but again the woodman refused to take it.

After a third dive into the water the river-fairy brought up the iron axe. 'That is mine,' cried the woodman, in great delight. The river-fairy was so pleased with the truthful way in which the man had behaved that she gave him the gold and silver axes also. The woodman went home to his cottage rejoicing.

1 Where did all this take place: (*a*) in the woodman's garden; (*b*) on a mountain-top; (*c*) near a river?

2 What happened to the woodman's axe?

3 The woodman was helped by: (*a*) his friend, who was a woodman; (*b*) the river-fairy; (*c*) the police?

4 After which dive did the river-fairy bring up the woodman's axe?

5 How was the woodman rewarded for being honest?

6 The river-fairy brought up the other axes because: (*a*) she did not know the difference between them and the iron axe; (*b*) she wanted to know how honest the man was; (*c*) she did not care very much what happened?

7 Write down the words that are true about the woodman: honest, poor, cunning, well-to-do, sly, artful, truthful, straightforward.

B **Common phrases**

We can say '*John behaved **in a stubborn way**'*, or we can say '*John behaved **like a mule**'*, because a mule is a stubborn animal.

Instead of the words in heavy type in the sentences below, write one of these: like a lamb; like a lion; like a tortoise; like a fox.

1 The captain fought **in a very brave way**.
2 The thief behaved **in a very cunning way**.
3 He went to school **in a very slow way**.
4 She went out **in a very quiet way**.

C **Sound-words**

These are words that when spoken aloud give you some idea of their meaning. Write sound-words in the spaces below.

The _____ of the wind and the _____ of the torrent were louder than the _____ of feet. Nobody heard the _____ of the bow, or the _____ of the arrow.

D **Nouns and adjectives**

1 Here are four **nouns**: plume, seat, road, voice.

Here are four **adjectives**: hoarse, waving, comfortable, major.

Put the **nouns** and the **adjectives** together in suitable pairs.
2 Now, do the same with these adjectives: bloodthirsty, offside, lovely, hidden.

Here are the nouns: princess, goal, pirate, wreck.

E **Contractions**

He's in a sentence means **he is**.

Example: *He's a big lad.*

What do the following mean:

that's	who've	o'er
doesn't	o'clock	'tis

TEST 14

(A) Read through the following passage very carefully, and then answer the questions.

Jack in Trouble

Jack lived with his widowed mother in a small cottage on the edge of a wood. They were very poor, and had to sell all their possessions in order to get food. The time came when all they had left to sell was a cow. Jack was told to drive the cow to market and sell her for as good a price as he could possibly get.

He set off, but he had not gone very far before he met a man who offered to buy the cow. But he did not offer Jack money. He offered a handful of beans, and simple Jack accepted them, giving the cow in exchange. When he reached home again, you can well believe how angry his mother was. She was so furious that she snatched the beans from the boy and threw them out of the window.

1 Write down the sentences that are true: (*a*) Jack and his mother were wealthy. (*b*) They lived in a tiny cottage. (*c*) Jack's father lived with them. (*d*) They were very poor indeed. (*e*) Their home was in a large town. (*f*) Jack's father was dead.

2 What had happened to all their possessions?

3 What was Jack going to do with the cow?

4 What was he offered for the cow?

5 Why was his mother so angry when he reached home?

6 Which of these things did she do? (*a*) She asked him to give her the beans. (*b*) She snatched the beans from him. (*c*) She took the beans to market.

7 Write down the sentences that are true: (*a*) The beans made a tasty meal. (*b*) The beans were flung through the window. (*c*) The beans were planted in the garden.

8 Write down the words that are true of Jack: foolish, clever, wise, stupid, simple, careful, keen.

(B) Synonyms

Look at the word **big**. Now look at the three words inside the brackets (ugly, large, broken). The word nearest in meaning to **big** is **large**.

Choose a word from those in brackets that is closest in meaning to the word in heavy type.

1 **joke** (song, book, jest)
2 **timid** (shy, bold, cheeky)
3 **bright** (dull, worn, shining)
4 **rip** (mend, lose, tear)
5 **new** (old, modern, broken)

(C) Alphabetical order

Here are the names of eight fish. Write them in alphabetical order.

pike, plaice, haddock, eel, cod, herring, whiting, trout.

(D) Homophones

Some words sound the same but are spelt differently.
Example: *Corn grew on the **plains/planes**.*
The correct word is **plains**. The other word **planes** means 'aeroplanes', or 'tools for woodwork'.
Choose the correct word each time.

I had an aunt who went on a **crews/cruise** to find a rare **flower/flour** for her garden. Soon she **new/knew** that the ship had **missed/mist** its way in the **missed/mist**.

(E) Rhyming words

Choose, from the words in brackets, the most suitable rhyming word to finish the lines in this poem:

> A little bit of blowing,
> A little bit of snow,
> A little bit of (**waiting/planting/growing**),
> And crocuses will (**spring/show/leap**);
> On every twig that's lovely,
> A new green leaf will spring,
> On every patient tree-top,
> A thrush will stop and (**chant/sing/warble**).

TEST 15

(A) Read through the following verses very carefully, and then answer the questions.

The Merry Mice

The merry mice stay in their holes
And hide there all the day;
But when the house is still at night,
The rogues come out and play.

They climb upon the pantry shelf,
And taste of all they please;
They drink the milk that's set for cream,
And nibble bread and cheese.

But if they chance to hear the cat,
Their feast will soon be done;
They scamper off to hide themselves
As fast as they can run.

Poet Unknown

1 When do the mice come out?
2 Where have they been all day?
3 What do they have for their supper?
4 How do we know that the things they eat are not on the floor?
5 What happens when they hear the cat coming? (*a*) They stand and make fun of her. (*b*) They change into lumps of cheese. (*c*) They run away in terror.
6 'The milk set for cream', means: (*a*) the milk left to catch the mice; (*b*) the milk in cream-coloured pans; (*c*) the milk that has been put into pans for making cream?
7 Why are the mice merry: (*a*) because someone has been telling them jokes; (*b*) because they can now come out from their hiding places; (*c*) because bells are ringing?
8 'Their feast will soon be done' means: (*a*) they will wait until they have finished; (*b*) they will scurry away before they have finished; (*c*) the cat will join in the feast?

(B) **Opposites**

The word **low** is the opposite of the word **high**. Complete the following sentences using the opposite of the word in heavy type.

1 Shall it be **war** or _____ between us?
2 The river is **deep** here, so find a _____ place.
3 Shall we stay here and **defend**, or shall we _____?
4 I thought you were my **friend**, but you are my _____.
5 They sought the treasure **near** and _____.

(C) **Gender**

Change the following sentences, which are about male animals, making them about female animals.

1 The **lion** roared in the jungle.
2 The **bull** was sent to market.
3 The **gander** swam on the pond.
4 The **drake** was fed each morning.

(D) **Punctuation**

Punctuation marks (. , ?) are missing from the following sentences. Write the sentences with the correct marks in them.

1 He asked a boy a girl and a soldier
2 Have you eggs and butter
3 Which will you have this or that
4 Were the hammer saw and nails still there

(E) **Odd one out**

In each of the following groups of words, one word is out of place because it has nothing to do with the others.

Example: *dog, cat, **lorry**, cow.*

Lorry is the odd one out because the other three are animals.

Find the odd one out in these:

1 waistcoat, boot, plimsoll, shoe
2 poker, tongs, saw, shovel
3 liner, tanker, tug, coach
4 toffee, caramel, biscuit, fudge

TEST 16

(A) Read through the following passage very carefully, and then answer the questions.

The Magic Trunk

It was a curious trunk. When the lock was pressed closed the trunk would fly. The merchant's son crouched down inside, pressed the lock, and lo! up flew the trunk through the chimney into the clouds, on and on, higher and higher. The lower part was cracked, which rather frightened him, for if it had broken in two, he would have had a nasty fall.

However, it descended safely, and he found himself in Turkey. He hid the trunk under a heap of dry leaves in a wood, and walked into the next town. He met a nurse carrying a little child in her arms. 'Hark ye, nurse,' quoth he. 'What palace is that with high windows close by the town?' 'The King's daughter dwells there,' replied the nurse.

1   What was so strange about the trunk?
2   Who was inside the trunk: (*a*) a road-sweeper; (*b*) the son of a merchant; (*c*) a space-traveller?
3   What happened when he pressed the lock?
4   How do we know that all this began inside a room?
5   Why was he rather frightened?
6   The trunk came down: (*a*) far away on the ocean; (*b*) in a foreign country; (*c*) on another planet?
7   Where was the trunk hidden?
8   He met: (*a*) a great band of soldiers; (*b*) a nurse with a baby; (*c*) some boys from school?

(B) Collective nouns

We speak of a **pair** of **shoes**. What words might we use to fill these spaces?

1 A _____ of firewood.
2 A _____ of sardines.
3 A _____ of chocolates.
4 A _____ of radishes.

(C) Crossword puzzles

Each of the answers to the crossword-puzzle clues begins with the letters CAN.

1 A Native American boat.   CAN _ _
2 A bird that sings sweetly.   CAN _ _ _
3 Used in warfare.   CAN _ _ _
4 Barges sail on this.   CAN _ _
5 This person eats human flesh.   CAN _ _ _ _ _
6 Gives a light.   CAN _ _ _

(D) Synonyms

The three words in the first brackets all have similar meanings. Choose one word from those in the second brackets that is similar in meaning to those in the first brackets.

Example: (*aid*, *support*, *help*) – (*assist*, paint, destroy)

1 (friend, playmate, comrade) – (enemy, companion, uncle)
2 (gap, chink, opening) – (fence, hole, hedge)
3 (lock, bolt, bar) – (cord, chain, cover)
4 (litter, lumber, waste) – (rubbish, food, goods)

(E) Put in order

Here are three sentences from a story, but they are not in the order in which things happened. Write the sentences in the order in which things took place.

1 The switch was pressed, and the rocket took off.
2 The door of the rocket was fastened tightly.
3 It soared away into the blue sky.

TEST 17

(A) Read through the following passage very carefully, and then answer the questions.

The Fishing Competition

The pier was crowded with young people waiting for the competition to begin. At last, the flag was hoisted, and everyone rushed to get to the best position. Splash! splash! Over went the lines. Soon, every fisherman was trying to watch his own float bobbing up and down on the water, and the floats of those around him.

There was a shout of joy, and Mike began to pull in his line. Was it a plaice or a dab on the end? Alas! It was only a bunch of seaweed that had caught on his hook. Sadly, he threw it back. Now the fun really began, as live catches were hauled up, and the little heaps of slithering, slippery fish began to grow in size. Some anglers could hardly wait to bait the hook with a wriggling worm. Time was going on!

1 Who was the competition for: (*a*) people of all ages; (*b*) adults only; (*c*) young people?

2 Which of these is true? (*a*) There were many competitors. (*b*) No one turned up. (*c*) Very few people were there.

3 Where was the event taking place?

4 What was the signal for beginning the competition?

5 (*a*) What did Mike haul up? (*b*) What might it have been?

6 Mike: (*a*) was very happy indeed; (*b*) did not care very much; (*c*) was very disappointed?

7 When caught, the fish were: (*a*) put into cans; (*b*) laid in heaps on the pier; (*c*) thrown back into the sea?

8 Some anglers were: (*a*) taking their time over things; (*b*) hurrying to get on with the fishing; (*c*) sitting down and doing nothing?

B **Answer the questions**

Write down the answers to the following questions.

1   What would you expect to find in a gallery?
2   What is the name of a place where young plants are grown?
3   What does a coastguard do?
4   Where would a game of tennis be played?

C **Using one word**

Write these sentences, but use one word instead of the words in heavy type:

1   Hans **lived in Holland**. Hans was _____.
2   He had **no parents**. He was an _____.
3   He was often **in need of food and water**. He was often _____ and _____.
4   He had **no friends**. He was _____.

D **Common phrases**

1   Paul said, 'The dinner makes my mouth water.' Did he mean: (*a*) I must wash before dinner; (*b*) there is only water for dinner; (*c*) it is such a nice dinner that I can hardly wait to begin?
2   The teacher said, 'You will get into hot water.' Did he mean: (*a*) you must have a bath; (*b*) you will get into trouble over something; (*c*) put the hot water into the teapot?
3   Mother said, 'Jane is hanging her head.' Did she mean: (*a*) Jane is making part of a puppet; (*b*) Jane is drying her hair; (*c*) Jane is sorry for what she has done?

E **Complete the story**

These words are missing from the story below:

time	masters	reading	stables
library	story	bad	horse

Write out the story, putting the words in the correct spaces.

Mary liked _____ *Black Beauty*, a book she had borrowed from the _____. It was the _____ of a _____ who had several _____, some good and some _____. The horse slept in many different _____ as _____ went on.

TEST 18

(A) Read through the following passage very carefully, and then answer the questions.

A Promise of Treasure

A soldier was marching along the highroad. He had a knapsack on his back, and a sword by his side, for he had been to the wars and was now returning home. On the road he met an old witch, and a very horrid creature she was.

'Good evening, Soldier!' said she. 'What a bright sword, and what a large knapsack! You shall have as much money for yourself as you wish.'

'Thanks, old witch!' cried the soldier.

'Do you see yonder large tree?' said the witch, pointing to one that stood close by. 'It is quite hollow within. Climb up to the top, and you will find a hole large enough for you to creep through, and thus you will get into the tree. I will tie a rope round your waist so that I can pull you up again when you call me.'

1 Where was the soldier coming from?
2 Name two things that he was carrying.
3 The soldier was: (a) travelling on horseback; (b) riding on a motorcycle; (c) marching along.
4 How do we know that the witch whom he met was not a pleasant person?
5 When did the meeting take place: (a) in the early morning; (b) in the evening; (c) in the afternoon?
6 What did the witch offer to give the soldier?
7 Why was it that the soldier was able to get into the tree?
8 How did the witch promise to get the soldier up again?
9 Which of these would make a good title for the story?
   (a) The Soldier Meets an Old Army Friend (b) A Meeting with a Strange, Old Creature (c) The Soldier Arrives Home Safely

B **Rhyming words**

The words **trees** and **please** both have the same sound. They are rhyming words.

Write these eight words in pairs, so that they rhyme:

dough	scythe	mow	lime
climb	plaice	blithe	base

C **Anagrams**

Look at the four letters E T A M. With them we can make several words. Here are some clues.

1 Not wild.
2 Eleven of these make a football _____.
3 The flesh of animals.

Now use the clues below to make words with these four letters: A E S T.

4 Opposite of west.
5 We sit on this.
6 '_____, light refreshments and minerals.'

D **Homonyms**

The word **wave** has more than one meaning. It may mean 'the **wave** on the **seashore**'; or it may mean 'the **wave** of the **hand**'.

Write down the words that can mean:

1 A large case or box, often filled with treasure; part of everyone's body.
2 Used to stop the sun from shining through the window; unable to see.
3 Used for lifting heavy weights; a bird with long legs.
4 The covering of a tree; the noise made by a dog.

E **Crossword puzzles**

Here are some crossword-puzzle clues. What are the answers?

1 A vegetable.   LE _ _
2 A horse and a lion have one.   MA _ _
3 What the bus conductor shouts.   'FA _ _ _ please.'
4 Beef, chicken and mutton.   ME _ _

TEST 19

(A) Read through the following passage very carefully, and then answer the questions.

The Changing of the Guard

John went to see the Changing of the Guard, and stood in the crowd outside Buckingham Palace, in London. The tall guardsmen in their scarlet tunics came marching along; their black bearskins made them seem even taller. The band played a lively tune, and everyone's feet went tap-tap-tapping in time to the music. The officers' swords gleamed in the sunshine, and so did the soldiers' bayonets and buttons. The men looked just like toy soldiers from a wooden box. Orders were shouted and obeyed smartly.

John wondered whether the Queen was up there at one of the high windows, watching her guardsmen. He saw a curtain move, but he was not near enough to see if it were Her Majesty.

Soon the Changing of the Guard was over. The crowd melted away, and John went home to lunch.

1 Where did the Changing of the Guard take place?
2 What other words are used for: (*a*) the Queen; (*b*) the soldiers?
3 What three things were shining in the sunlight?
4 What was John wondering while this was going on?
5 What made the soldiers seem very tall indeed? (*a*) They were marching on the pavement. (*b*) The people looking on were dwarfs. (*c*) They wore tall black hats.
6 How do we know that there was music to be heard?
7 How do we know this was happening: (*a*) in the morning; (*b*) in England?
8 'The crowd melted away.' Does this mean: (*a*) the people all disappeared; (*b*) they walked away; (*c*) they really melted?

B **Abbreviations and contractions**

'John lives in **Oakwood Pl.**' **Pl.** is short for **Place**.

Write these shortened words in full:

1 Sheila lives in Princes **Rd.**
2 Stephen lives in George **St.**
3 Joy lives in Grange **Gdns**.
4 Susan lives in Wood **Ave.**
5 Tony lives in Hope **Sq.**

C **Proper nouns**

All proper nouns (special names) begin with a **capital letter**.

Rewrite these sentences, beginning each proper noun with a capital letter:

1 peter smith is a pupil at st stephens primary school.
2 His teacher is mr rogers.
3 The river thames flows through London, England.

D **Word groups**

John, Anne, Michael and Jean are all **names**. Write one word that describes each of the following groups of words.

1 spring, summer, autumn, winter
2 Monday, Tuesday, Wednesday, Friday
3 Mars, Venus, Jupiter, Saturn
4 silk, nylon, tweed, velvet
5 coal, coke, peat, paraffin

E **Synonyms**

From the words inside the brackets in each sentence, write down the one that is nearest in meaning to the word in heavy type.

Example: **level**. *The ground was (bumpy, swampy, **flat**).*

1 **curious**   What a (mean, strange, happy) thing to do.
2 **modern**   That carving is (new, ugly, old).
3 **mariner**   The (explorer, seaman, baby) walked on the quay.
4 **dusk**   They were home by (morning, twilight, midday).

TEST 20

(A) Read through the following verses very carefully, and then answer the questions.

Spring

I am coming, I am coming!
Hark! the little bee is humming.
See the lark is soaring high
In the blue and sunny sky;
And the gnats are on the wing,
Wheeling round in airy ring.

See the yellow catkins cover
All the slender willows over;
And on banks of mossy green
Star-like primroses are seen;
And their clustering leaves below,
White and purple violets blow.

Mary Howitt

1 Who is saying 'I am coming': (*a*) the Fairy Queen; (*b*) the season of Spring; (*c*) Old Man Winter?

2 Here are some colours used in the poem: blue, yellow, green, purple. Write them with the correct nouns from this list: violets, catkins, sky, banks.

3 Write down the words that tell us what each of these is doing: (*a*) The bee is _____. (*b*) The lark is _____. (*c*) The gnats are _____.

4 How can we tell that it was a warm and pleasant day?

5 Why do you think the primroses were said to be star-like?

6 Write down the sentences that are true: (*a*) The violets were all of one colour. (*b*) There were many leaves, in bunches. (*c*) It was easy to see the violets. (*d*) The leaves were few in number. (*e*) There were violets of two colours. (*f*) The violets were half hidden. (*g*) The lark was flying high in the sky. (*h*) The willows had no catkins on them.

(B) Sound-words

Write sound-words in the spaces in the sentences below:

The _____ of broken glass followed the _____ of the bullet as the rifle _____. The soldiers were awakened by the _____ of the bugle.

(C) Nouns and adjectives

1 Here are four **nouns**: elf, mountain, bird, eel.

And here are four other words, one to describe each of the words above: feathered, snow-capped, tiny, wriggling.

Put the nouns and the **adjectives** together in suitable pairs.

2 Now do the same with these **adjectives**: dainty, fierce, barking, sugary.

Here are the **nouns**: tea, bull, dog, sprite.

(D) Proverbs

Finish these proverbs, or well-known sayings:

1 A miss is as good as _____ _____.
2 Don't count your chickens _____ _____ _____.
3 Look before _____ _____.
4 A friend in need _____ _____ _____ _____.

(E) Relative pronouns

Look at these sentences:

1 The boy came first.   2 He is young.

We can make them into one sentence by using the word **who**. We can write 'The boy **who** came first is young.'

Join each of the sentences below by using **who**, **that**, **whose** or **whom**.

1 This is the cap. It is torn.
2 I am the boy. You saw me.
3 She is a teacher. Her laptop computer has been stolen.
4 I saw the salesman. He called yesterday.

TEST 21

(A) Read through the following passage very carefully, and then answer the questions.

Holiday Plans

In March, the family sat down at the table and began to talk about the summer holiday. Where should they go this year? That was the question that had to be answered. Should they go to the seaside, or to the country? Did they prefer fun on the farm, or basking on a beach? The children soon settled that. With one voice they cried, 'Seaside, please!'

'Let's go somewhere where there's good swimming,' said Sally, who had just won her Life-Saving Certificate. 'And good fishing,' said Alan, who had been given a smart rod for his birthday. 'What about mountain climbing?' Paul asked. He had been to Switzerland the year before with the Scout troop.

'Mother and I just want to sit on a beach,' said Father. 'That is, if you don't mind, of course.'

'Two deckchairs for a fortnight for Mother and Father. Then everyone will be happy,' the children cried.

1 Why was the family holding the meeting?
2 What two kinds of places did they first think about?
3 Which did they decide upon?
4 'Basking on a beach' means: (a) climbing up a tree; (b) lying in the sun at the seaside; (c) sitting in a basket chair?
5 Why was Sally keen on swimming?
6 Why was Alan keen to fish?
7 Why did Paul want to go mountain climbing?
8 Why did the children say 'Two deckchairs for Mother and Father': (a) because their parents always sit in deckchairs; (b) because they were going for a sail on a boat; (c) because their parents wanted to sit on the beach and rest?

B Who are these characters?

Write down the names of these people whom we meet in books and poems:

1 He was a merry old soul.
2 A young wizard with a lightning-shaped scar.
3 A black mouse with gloves and red shorts.
4 An egg who fell off a wall.
5 A young boy who found a genie in a lamp.

C Making new words

If we chop the first letter off **a place where we go skating** – RINK – we get **something we use when writing** – INK. (RINK becomes INK.)

Do the same with these:

1 'A place where we play games' becomes 'Noah's ship'.
2 'A sea vessel' becomes 'a part of the body'.
3 'Something we open to go into the garden' becomes 'what we did with our food at our last meal'.
4 'Part of the foot' becomes 'a wriggling fish'.
5 'A wild beast's den' becomes 'that which we breathe'.
6 'One who cleans chimneys' becomes 'to cry'.

D Anagrams

In each of the cases below, rearrange the letters to make the name of a **bird**.

Example: *WAKH becomes HAWK.*

1 WORC   3 REWN   5 NERT
2 NAWS   4 CKDU   6 KRAL

E Capital letters

Read through the passage below very carefully and then write it down as it should be written, in verse. Begin each line with a capital letter.

Now to the banquet we press, now for the eggs and the ham, now for the mustard and cress, now for the strawberry jam.

TEST 22

(A) Read through the following passage very carefully, and then answer the questions.

The Racing Car

The boys first chose a soapbox for the body. They took four wheels from an old pram on a rubbish heap, found some long nails and a length of rope, and they were ready to begin building the racing car. There were many mistakes, and sore fingers, before the Silver Arrow was ready for its trial run. They hauled it to the top of a steep slope, climbed aboard and pushed off.

The car gathered speed and went rushing downwards. All was well for the first minute. Then Jack gasped, 'The bend at the bottom!' Yes, they had forgotten all about the great curve. It was coming nearer, nearer. There was not the slightest chance of steering the Silver Arrow at that speed. With a screeching sound it left the road and burst through the wire fence.

1　What was the body of the car made of: (*a*) an old pram; (*b*) an empty soapbox; (*c*) part of a real car?

2　Where were the wheels found?

3　How were the parts fastened together?

4　Why were there sore fingers: (*a*) because the boys were biting their nails; (*b*) because they had hit their hands with the hammer; (*c*) because they had burnt them?

5　Where did the boys go to test the car?

6　Which of these is true? (*a*) It went quicker and quicker. (*b*) The car refused to start. (*c*) It overturned at the start.

7　What did Jack suddenly remember?

8　Which of these is true? (*a*) The car ran into a lorry. (*b*) It ran on to the pavement. (*c*) It crashed through a fence at the side of the road.

(B) **Homophones**

Some words sound the same, but are spelt differently.
Example: *The old **which**/**witch** flew away on her broomstick.* The correct word is **witch**.

Choose the correct word each time.

1 He tried in **vain/vane** to find the treasure.
2 He tramped over many a hill and **veil/vale**.
3 He **herd/heard** many stories of where it was hidden.
4 At last he saw a blue **buoy/boy** floating on the sea.

Ⓒ Synonyms

Look at the word **broad**. Now look at the three words inside the brackets (wide, narrow, empty). The word nearest in meaning to **broad** is **wide**.

Choose a word from those in brackets that is closest in meaning to the word in heavy type.

1 **sportsman** (explorer, countryman, footballer)
2 **ship** (vase, scuttle, vessel)
3 **brook** (river, stream, ocean)
4 **field** (meadow, jungle, heath)
5 **throw** (catch, taste, hurl)

Ⓓ Opposites

The word **hot** is the opposite of the word **cold**. Write the following sentences using the opposite of the word in heavy type.

1 Your wood is **smooth**, and his is _____.
2 They travelled over **land** and _____.
3 It is a question of **right** and _____.
4 The magic rose bloomed in **winter** and _____.
5 The sun shines **often**; the wind blows _____.

Ⓔ Complete the poem

Choose, from the words in brackets, the most suitable rhyming word to finish the lines in this poem.

> Sing hey! Sing hey!
> For Christmas (**eve/day/morn**);
> Twine mistletoe and holly,
> For friendship grows
> In winter (**time/months/snows**),
> And so let's all be (**merry/happy/jolly**).

TEST 23

(A) Read through the following passage very carefully, and then answer the questions.

Tony's Travels

There were three ways in which Tony could travel to school: by bus, by train or on the underground. Each of these ways held something special. The bus journey was interesting because one passed shops and markets, human beings, traffic lights, other buses and cars. The train was exciting because one could run up and down the corridor – if the ticket inspector wasn't on the prowl, as he usually was, knowing what a naughty cargo he was carrying.

The underground train was the quickest. Tony used this only if he had something important to do when he reached school – something that had to be done, unpleasant though it might be, such as finishing last night's homework. The fare to Good-hampton was exactly the same whichever way he travelled.

1 How do we know that Tony lived some distance away from his school?
2 What were the three ways of travelling?
3 Which journey cost the most?
4 Why was Tony happy when he travelled by bus?
5 Why did the ticket inspector have to prowl about on the train?
6 Which was the quickest way of travelling?
7 Why did Tony sometimes go by underground?
8 In what town was Tony's school?
9 From the list below choose words that describe the journey (*a*) by bus; (*b*) by train; (*c*) by underground.

| quick | attractive | speedy | thrilling |
| enchanting | rapid | fast | uninteresting |

B Odd one out

In each of the following groups of words, one word is out of place because it has nothing to do with the others.

Example: *cow, horse, **lion**, sheep.*

Lion is the odd one out, because all the others are tame animals.

Find the odd one out in these:

1 chocolate, fudge, pizza, ice cream
2 carrot, chicken, steak, kidney
3 carpet, settee, shirt, rug
4 coffee, cocoa, lemonade, tea

C Apostrophes

Look at this sentence: *This is **Susans** doll.* There is something missing – an **apostrophe** – to show that the doll belongs to Susan. It should have been: *This is **Susan's** doll.*

Write the apostrophe in its place in these sentences:

1 I went to Betty Browns party.
2 I am David Copperfields aunt.
3 Where is Oliver Twists gruel?
4 Long John Silvers parrot died.

D Past tense

Look at this sentence: '*Bill **scores** a goal.*' It is happening **now**. But if we write '*Bill **scored** a goal*', we are showing that it happened in the past as if it happened **in the past**.

All the sentences below are written as if they are happening **now**. Write them as if they happened **in the past**.

1 Jean **makes** a cake.
2 Father **cleans** the windows.
3 Mother **drives** a car.
4 The hen **lays** an egg.
5 She **sees** the picture.
6 The dog **barks** at the stranger.

E Alphabetical order

Write the names of these foods in alphabetical order:

cheese, coffee, bacon, bread, biscuits, cocoa, chocolate, butter.

TEST 24

(A) Read through the following passage very carefully, and then answer the questions.

Jane's Problem

There were half a dozen dolls in the window. They were all on one shelf. Each doll was dressed in the clothes of the country from which it came. There was a Japanese doll in a kimono, and a doll in the grass skirt of Fiji. A third wore the kilt of Scotland, and a fourth had on the tall, black hat of Wales. Next came a Native American doll, which, wore a coloured blanket, and shoes called moccasins. Last of all was the English doll, a neat little girl in school uniform.

It was going to be very hard for Jane to choose one doll from this charming collection. Each had something that made it seem nicer than the others. Yet, only one could be chosen. She had money for only one. Was it to be the biggest, or the prettiest?

1   Which of these is true? (*a*) There were many, many dolls. (*b*) There was one doll. (*c*) There were six dolls.
2   Which of these is true? (*a*) They were all dressed alike. (*b*) They were dressed in different kinds of clothes. (*c*) Their clothes could not be seen.
3   What did Jane have to choose?
4   Where was the kimono: (*a*) on the doll's body; (*b*) on her feet; (*c*) on her head?
5   Where were the moccasins: (*a*) on the doll's feet; (*b*) on her back; (*c*) on her head?
6   Here are the countries: Japan, Wales, Scotland, Fiji, England, North America. And here are the clothes: grass skirt, kilt, kimono, black hat, moccasins, school uniform. Put them into their correct pairs.
7   Which doll wore a coloured blanket?
8   Which doll do you think Jane will choose? Why?

(B) **More than one**

The sentence 'The boy used the long nail' means **one** boy and **one** nail. But the sentence 'The **boys** used the long **nails**' means **more than one** boy and **more than one** nail.

Change the sentences below so that they mean more than one.

1 The mouse hid on the shelf.
2 The driver drove the car very fast.
3 The sheep fed on the hillside.
4 The gun fired the shell.

(C) **Compound words**

Here are two words: **paper** and **weight**. If we put them together we can make a new word **paperweight**.

From these eight words make four new words, using each once only:

spoon	sea	tea	mill
gull	knee	water	cap

(D) **Adjectives**

Finish the sentences below by choosing the correct word from these:

heavy	light	sweet
hard	precious	sour

1 Sugar is _____.   4 Gold is _____.
2 Lead is _____.   5 Cork is _____.
3 Vinegar is _____.   6 Iron is _____.

(E) **Complete the story**

These words are missing from the story below:

wanderings	humans	exciting
animals	strange	rabbit-hole

Write out the story, using the words to fill the spaces.

It was an _____ book, all about Alice falling down a _____, and of the _____ things that happened in her _____ underground. Before she awoke from her dream she met many _____ who spoke like _____.

TEST 25

(A) Read through the following verses very carefully, and then answer the questions.

The Moon

The moon has a face like the clock in the hall;
She shines on thieves on the garden wall,
On streets and fields and harbour quays,
And birdies asleep in the forks of the trees.

The squalling cat and the squeaking mouse,
The howling dog by the door of the house,
The bat that lies in bed at noon,
All love to be out by the light of the moon.

But all of the things that belong to the day
Cuddle to sleep to be out of the way;
And flowers and children close their eyes,
Till up in the morning the sun shall rise.

R. L. Stevenson

1 Why has the moon a face like the clock in the hall: (*a*) because it is seen only at night; (*b*) because they both make a ticking sound; (*c*) because it is round, like a clock-face?

2 Why are the birdies asleep in the 'forks of the trees': (*a*) because they are safer there; (*b*) because they have had no supper; (*c*) because they are afraid of the moon?

3 Finish these sentences with sound-words from the poem:
(*a*) The cat is _____. (*b*) The dog is _____.
(*c*) The mouse is _____.

4 What are 'harbour quays': (*a*) the keys that open the harbour; (*b*) places where ships can tie up; (*c*) the streets of the town?

5 The bat is in its bed at _____ o'clock. Finish this sentence.

6 Who is sleeping at night?

7 What will wake them up?

8 Choose a new title for the poem from: (*a*) All the Fun of the Fair (*b*) A Dangerous Voyage (*c*) When Day is Done

(B) Spot the mistakes

There are mistakes in each of the following sentences. Write the sentences correctly by changing the wrong word.

1   The work was did too quickly.
2   Give me them sweets at once.
3   The cat was laying on the roof.
4   Whose toys is those?

(C) Word-doubles

We call 'neck and neck' a word-double.

Example: *They finished the race **neck and neck**.*

Finish the word-doubles in the following sentences.

1   He shouted **again** and _____.
2   I shall come **by and** _____.
3   The boy rolled **over and** _____.
4   The top spun **round and** _____.

(D) Anagrams

Look at the four letters E D R A. With these four letters we can make several words. Here are some clues:

1   We sometimes begin a letter '_____ Sir'.
2   To take a risk.
3   Children sometimes say '_____ me a story'.

Now make words with these four letters: I V E L.

4   Wicked.
5   She wore a pretty _____ on her hat.
6   I hope that the Prince and Princess will _____ happily ever after.

(E) Contractions

I'm in a sentence means **I am**.

Example: ***I'm** going out.*

What do these mean:

can't	didn't	don't
isn't	there's	I've

TEST 26

(A) Read through the following passage very carefully, and then answer
the questions.

The Great Adventure

A troop of Boy Scouts was marching down the road. Left, right, left,
right – they kept in perfect step. The bugles blared and the drums
beat. A flag was carried along. Four brawny lads hauled the big trek-
cart that was laden with goods for the camp. There were things to
eat and things to drink, things to wear and things to use – a great
mixture of flour, lemonade, pails, hats, tea, sugar, ginger-beer, poles
and water. All these were separate, of course. It would have been fun
if they had suddenly got mixed up together.

At the end of the road three lorries were waiting. The joyful lads
piled aboard, and to the sound of singing from half a hundred
young voices, the convoy started. The Great Adventure had begun.
There were fourteen days ahead; glorious days of fun and frolic!

1 How many Scouts were there: (*a*) more than one could
count; (*b*) very few; (*c*) about fifty?
2 How can we tell that the Scouts were marching smartly?
3 What was the 'Great Adventure'? Was it (*a*) going to camp;
(*b*) going to the war; (*c*) going to school?
4 How were they going to travel: (*a*) by railway;
(*b*) by road, in lorries; (*c*) by aeroplane?
5 How do we know that there was a band playing?
6 Which is true? (*a*) Their goods were carried by hand. (*b*) They
had gone on ahead. (*c*) They were pulled along in a cart.
7 For how long were they going to be away?
8 What were the things (*a*) to eat; (*b*) to drink; (*c*) to wear;
(*d*) to use?

(B) **Put in order**

Here are three sentences from a story, but they are not in the order in which things happened. Write them in the correct order.

1 The plane circled over the city.
2 The pilot climbed into the cockpit of the aeroplane.
3 Parcels of food were dropped to the starving people.

(C) **Who does what?**

Write the correct definition for each of the words in heavy type.

1 A **plumber**   (*a*) sells plums; (*b*) mends broken water-pipes; (*c*) sells lumber.
2 A **thief**   (*a*) is a person who collects fees; (*b*) steals things that belong to other people; (*c*) watches clocks.
3 A **tailor**   (*a*) makes and repairs clothing; (*b*) drives a tanker; (*c*) passes the time thinking.
4 A **jockey**   (*a*) plays a game with a ball and stick; (*b*) rides a horse in a race; (*c*) keeps a shop.

(D) **Prefixes**

Look at these two sentences: *This bridge is **safe**. That bridge is **unsafe**.* By adding **un** to **safe** the word becomes the exact opposite in meaning.

Do the same with these sentences. To make the opposite in each case, choose from these parts of words: **un**, **mis**, **im**, **in**.

1 You are very **kind**, but Mary is _____.
2 This way is **direct**, but that way is _____.
3 Peter will **behave**, but Paul will _____.
4 Jill is **polite**, but Linda is _____.

(E) **Using one word**

Write the sentences below, but use one word instead of the words in heavy type.

As the sun **went out of sight** behind the hills, Robin Hood and his band **came into view**. The **men and women who were in chains** hoped that they would soon be **set at liberty**, so that they might return **at once** to their **houses, huts and cottages**.

TEST 27

(A) Read through the following passage very carefully, and then answer the questions.

Jolly Roger

Nearer and nearer came the galleon. The crew of the brig found their joy turned to sorrow, for a flag appeared at the mast-head; the hated and feared Jolly Roger. The white skull and crossbones stood out clearly against the black flag.

There was not a moment to lose! The brig's crew sprang to life, and hurried below for weapons. They came on deck again with a mixed collection – cutlasses, pikes, swords, daggers and pistols. The brass gun in the bows was loaded, and the muzzle pointed towards the pirate ship, which was now very near indeed.

No one expected any mercy if they fell into the hands of Fork-Beard and his band of ruffians. Walking the plank! That was the way many a crew had met its fate when captured.

1 Why did the crew of the brig suddenly become very sad?
2 Where did the Jolly Roger fly: (*a*) from a sailor's hands; (*b*) from a porthole; (*c*) from the mast-head?
3 The pirates' flag was: (*a*) red, white and blue; (*b*) black, with a skull and crossbones; (*c*) green, with yellow birds?
4 The crew 'sprang to life'. Does this mean: (*a*) they had been dead, but came to life; (*b*) they sprang overboard; (*c*) they all rushed to get weapons?
5 Which of these is true? (*a*) The weapons were stored below decks. (*b*) They were already in the sailors' hands. (*c*) They were already piled on deck.
6 How were captured sailors often put to death by pirates?

B **A or An?**

Example: *a song*, *a wolf*, **an** *otter*, **an** *egg*.

Write **a** or **an** in the spaces below.

1 She had _____ pretty doll, and _____ ugly one.
2 _____ underground passage led to _____ beach.
3 _____ ant and _____ bumble bee were caught.
4 Can we change _____ Airedale for _____ terrier?
5 _____ friend of mine eats _____ apple or _____ pear each day.

C **Homonyms**

The word **fine** has more than one meaning. It may mean 'a **fine** we have to pay for doing wrong', or '**fine** weather'.

Write down the words than can mean:

1 Belonging to me; where coal is dug; something floating in the sea, which explodes on striking a ship.
2 Out of harm's way; where valuable things are kept.
3 Not heavy; helps us to see in the darkness.
4 To write one's name at the end of a letter; hangs outside an inn or other building.

D **Fill in the blanks**

Write the correct letters to finish these sentences:

1 The aeroplane was left in its **h _ _ _ _ r**.
2 They saw the cowboy film at the new **c _ _ _ _ a**.
3 They had lunch at a lonely **c _ _ é**.
4 The Roman remains were in the **m _ _ _ _ m**.
5 There was a pantomime at the local **t _ _ _ _ _ e**.

E **Rhyming words**

The words **he** and **she** both have the same sound. They are rhyming words.

Write these eight words in pairs, so that they rhyme:

through	blue	duty	stuff
clear	tough	steer	beauty

TEST 28

(A) Read through the following passage very carefully, and then answer the questions.

In the Depths of the Sea

The giant octopus left its cave, and moved along the reef. Somehow or other the news was flashed to every living thing. Most of them crawled, swam or scuttled for shelter. The smaller fish found cracks and crevices in which to hide. The shrimps and prawns darted here and there in panic, and the crabs and lobsters slithered away to dark corners, to wait until Old Killer had gone.

One alone stayed to do battle. This was the great eel who had long fancied himself against the King of the Reef, and was waiting for a chance to defeat the octopus and take over his crown. The eel depended upon his swift rushes and strong jaws to overcome the eight long arms, each covered with dozens of suckers that could grip an enemy and draw it to its parrot-like beak.

1 Where did all this happen?
2 The octopus has two other names. What are they?
3 What was the bad news that the other creatures soon heard?
4 What did each creature have to do as quickly as possible?
5 Where did the small fish go?
6 What happened to the shrimps and prawns?
7 What did the great eel make up his mind to do?
8 How did the eel win his battles with other fish?
9 What made the octopus such a dangerous enemy to fight?
10 The eel wanted to take over the 'octopus's crown'. Does this mean: (a) he wanted to wear a crown that the octopus was wearing; (b) he wanted to dive about in the water; (c) he wanted to become King of the Reef?
11 What was the reef: (a) a pool in the rocks; (b) a sandy bank; (c) a great ledge of rocks under the sea?

B **Proverbs**

Complete these proverbs, or well-known sayings:

1 Too many cooks _____ _____ _____.
2 Where there's a will _____ _____ _____.
3 More haste _____ _____.
4 Early to bed and early to rise _____ _____ _____ _____

_____ _____ _____.

C **What are they?**

Jill, Sally, Elizabeth and Jane are all **girls' names**. Write down one word that describes each of the following groups:

1 pine, fir, spruce, larch
2 car, taxi, coach, carriage
3 trumpet, bugle, drum, triangle
4 King, Queen, Prince, Princess

D **Proper nouns**

All proper nouns (special names) begin with a **capital letter**.

Rewrite these sentences, beginning each proper noun with a capital letter:

1 mary finished reading *treasure island*.
2 She took the book to london with her.
3 She lent it to jane, and received *billy bunter* instead.
4 The book had been given to jane for christmas.

E **Synonyms**

From the words inside the brackets in each sentence, write down the one that is nearest in meaning to the word in heavy type.

Example: *true*. *This is an (idle, **exact**, awkward) story.*

1 **chill** Outside a (pleasant, gentle, cold) wind blew.
2 **brook** Let us go and fish in the miller's (pond, stream, lake).
3 **sweet** This tea is too (sugary, bitter, strong).
4 **scholar** I am a (master, pupil, tutor) at the new school.

TEST 29

(A) Read through the following passage very carefully, and then answer the questions.

On Private Property

The notice said plainly: PRIVATE, KEEP OUT. Each time Tim saw the words they seemed to say 'It doesn't mean you; come in.' At last he could stand it no longer. He looked up and down the road. There was no one in sight. He scrambled through the ditch, then pushed his way through a hole in the fence and into the wood.

The bushes were wet and thorny, and each one tried to grasp him as he went by. But he pressed on until he found the clearing. There was the black-painted hut. He went towards it carefully, and tried to peep in through a window, but it was boarded up. The door, too, looked solid, and there was no sign of a handle. Suddenly, from inside came the sound of voices.

1 What was painted on the noticeboard?
2 Which of these is true? (*a*) Tim didn't see the notice. (*b*) Tim did as the notice told him. (*c*) Tim thought it said 'COME IN'.
3 Why did he look up and down the road?
4 Through what two things did he pass to get inside?
5 The bushes tried to hold him: (*a*) because they were thorny; (*b*) because they were very high; (*c*) because they were on fire?
6 What was 'the clearing': (*a*) a ring of people; (*b*) a place where the trees had been cleared away; (*c*) something he had lost in the bushes?
7 Which of these did he see: (*a*) a tin hut with a thatched roof; (*b*) a fortress; (*c*) a hut that was painted black?
8 Why couldn't he see through the window?
9 What sound came from inside?

(B) **Anagrams**

Rearrange the letters of the words below to make the name of an insect.

Example: *EBE becomes BEE.*

1 AFEL   3 PAWS   5 NTA
2 TANG   4 THMO

(C) **Capital letters**

Read through the following passage very carefully, and then write it down as it should be written, in verse. Begin each line with a capital letter.

Now for the tea of our host, now for the raspberry bun, now for the muffin and toast, now for the gay Sally Lunn.

(D) **Who are these characters?**

Write down the names of these people whom we meet in books and poems:

1 He climbed a beanstalk.
2 He was the strongest man who ever lived.
3 He was the headmaster at a school for wizards.
4 He was a boy who grew up in the jungle with wolves.
5 She had a wicked stepmother and two cruel sisters.

(E) **Contractions**

Instead of 'He said **he would** do it', we can write 'He said **he'd** do it.'

Write out the following sentences using short ways of writing the words that are in heavy type.

1 **All is** well that ends well.
2 **I shall not** help you with your homework.
3 **We have** come home.
4 **It is** Christmas Day tomorrow.
5 **There is** a 29 bus in the distance.

TEST 30

(A) Read through the following verses very carefully, and then answer the questions.

The Cow

The friendly cow all red and white
I love with all my heart,
She gives me cream with all her might
To eat with apple-tart.

She wanders lowing here and there,
And yet she cannot stray,
All in the pleasant open air,
The pleasant light of day.

And blown by all the winds that pass,
And wet with all the showers,
She walks amid the meadow grass,
And eats the meadow flowers.

R. L. Stevenson

1   Why does the child in the poem love the cow so much:
    (*a*) because the cow lets the child ride on her back; (*b*) because
    the cow pulls a cart along; (*c*) because the cow gives milk that
    is made into cream?
2   How do we know that the weather is not always warm and
    pleasant for the cow?
3   How do we know that the cow is not silent while she walks?
4   All this is happening: (*a*) on a summer's day; (*b*) in a foggy
    autumn; (*c*) on a winter's night?
5   How do we know that the cow is not feeding high up on the
    mountainside?
6   If Friesian cows are black and white, Jersey cows are light
    brown, Hereford cows are red and white, and Red Polls are
    red all over, which is the cow in the poem?
7   Look at these words: friendly, peaceful, savage, kindly,
    dangerous, fierce, lovable. Write down those that describe
    the cow.

B **Homophones**

Some words sound the same, but are spelt differently.

Example: *The girl rode/road the pony.* The correct word is **rode**.

Write out this passage, choosing the correct words.

The **seen/scene** made us **stare/stair** in wonder through the **pane/pain**. The **tied/tide** was out, and the ship was gone from the **pier/peer**.

C **Past tense**

Look at this sentence: *Bill **makes** a run from the first ball.* It is happening **now**. *Bill **made** a run from the first ball* means that it happened **in the past**.

Write the following sentences as if they had already happened.

1 The miller **grinds** his corn.
2 Miss Smith **teaches** the children.
3 The airman **flies** over the school.
4 The grass **is** green in the meadows.
5 The birds **nest** in the trees.

D **Apostrophes**

Look at this sentence: *This is Johns bat.* The apostrophe is missing. The sentence should have been: *This is John's bat.*

Write out these sentences, putting the apostrophe in its correct place:

1 Where is Lucys locket?
2 Come to Black Beautys stable.
3 I am going to the Mad Hatters tea-party.
4 This is Wee Willie Winkies house.

E **Put in order**

Write these in order of size, beginning each time with the smallest:

1 football, golf ball, bowl, tennis ball
2 eagle, seagull, blue tit, starling
3 peke, Alsatian, bulldog, St Bernard
4 butterfly, dragonfly, bee, ant